GCSE English

Style and Purpose

BRAINSTORM

John Nield

Folens Publishers

Contents

First published 2000 by Folens Limited.
United Kingdom: Folens Publishers, Apex Business Centre, Boscombe Road, Dunstable, LU5 4RL.
Email: folens@folens.com

Ireland: Folens Publishers, Greenhills Road, Tallaght, Dublin 24.
Email: info@folens.ie

Poland: JUKA, ul. Renesansowa 38, Warsaw 01-905.

Editor: Helen Banbury
Layout artist: Suzanne Ward
Cover design: Ed Gallagher
Illustrations: Chantal Kees

Acknowledgements
p35   'Lara Blasts Rivals into Cyber-space' by Chris Barrie © The Guardian, reproduced by kind permission of The Guardian.
p37   'Anthem for Tombed youth' by Charlotte Raven © The Guardian, reproduced by kind permission of The Guardian.
p46   Shelter leaflet and first photograph reproduced by kind permission of Shelter.
       Second photograph reproduced by kind permission of The Stock Market Photo Agency Inc.

© 2000 Folens Limited, on behalf of the author.
Reprinted 2000, 2001.

Every effort has been made to trace the copyright holders of material used in this publication. If any copyright holder has been overlooked, we should be pleased to make any necessary arrangements.

British Library Cataloguing in Publication Data. A catalogue record for this publication is available from the British Library.

ISBN 1 84163 581-2

Introduction

The National Curriculum 2000 English Orders, upon which all English GCSE examination syllabuses are predicated, insists that all students should experience a wide range of different types of reading and writing. This book aims to help teachers to give students strategies and scaffolding to support their efforts to compose their writing at exam level. The frames enable the least and most able to make more focused use of their skills as readers and writers, by giving them a scaffold, which can be taken away when they are more robust and confident in their own abilities. In essence, it makes the most able answer the specific question, while giving the least able a secure framework within which to locate their own ideas and efforts.

It is, however, the students in the mid-range of ability who stand to gain most from this book. They invariably lack the discourse structures and markers, which are too often taken for granted. This book supplies those markers; gives other pointers as to how various types of writing differ; and develops confidence through adopting good practice.

Each Unit contains five sheets:

Sheet 1: **Key Points and Advice**
This sheet provides a quick check-list of ideas, advice and skills required for the particular form of writing.

Sheet 2: **Generating Ideas**
This sheet provides a sample task with room for 'brainstorming' and/or sequencing.

Sheet 3: **Ideas and Markers**
This sheet provides further ideas for content, plus key phrases or discourse markers which form part of the writer's 'palette', from which they can pick the best words possible.

Sheet 4: **A Writing Frame**
This sheet provides the actual frame for the essay with key markers and phrases already included.

Sheet 5: **Further Practice**
This sheet provides a further passage with some text omitted for weaker students, or for reinforcement work.

There is an optional disk (PC format) which is for student and teacher use. It contains the same key elements and sheets as the book itself, but has additional features, which will be of use to many students, particularly those who find extended writing difficult, or struggle to employ the ideas required for each piece of coursework or exam task.

The disk contains:
- further tasks for extended practice in the key writing areas
- help with completing these further tasks (word-banks, possible ideas, etc.).

Teacher input
Teachers can also modify the tasks and text, according to the needs and abilities of their students. They might also wish to alter text to suit a particular task that has been practised in class, or delete a line they find unhelpful. Additionally, they can add extra lines of advice or key points that come up during the work. However, there is no necessity to do this, as the disk is designed to be used by students as it stands – and any modification is entirely at the discretion of the teacher concerned.

Printing
A key feature of the disk is the capacity for students to print out their finished work from the 'Frames' pages. When they do so, the boxes will disappear, leaving continuous prose text.

Finally, the disk provides a useful resource for students who will benefit from the extra features it offers, and stimulates their own enthusiasm for using a keyboard and screen for English work. Of course, it is recognised that computer-generated work has limitations for assessment purposes, but it can be a key factor in building skills and scaffolding ideas.

How to install the program
From the Start button, go to Run. At the prompt, type the drive letter for your CD drive + :\setup (e.g. D:\setup) and press Return/Enter.

Writing to Argue

Key Points and Advice

Writing to argue means that you must:

◆ express a point about a subject or issue
◆ be aware, however, that there is an alternative viewpoint
◆ not simply put forward what *you* believe; but rather try to counter alternative points that have been made, or could be made.

An argument is effective if it convinces the reader or gives the reader cause to reconsider an opinion.

Read the following points carefully before you apply them to the given title or exam question. Then work through them methodically, one by one; remember, they will form part of the Mark Scheme for your exams.

1. There are two sides to every argument, so begin with a brainstorming session which lists arguments for both sides.

2. Think about your arguments carefully.

3. Organise your arguments clearly (from your brainstorm).

4. When you write, begin with an opening statement which uses the title.

5. Make a point at the beginning of every paragraph and build on it. Make your paragraphs in favour of your statement long and detailed. Make your paragraphs against the idea short and dismissive.

6. Use discourse markers (e.g. *'however,' 'moreover', 'as you can see'*, etc.)

7. Use some, or all, of the following:

   ● rhetorical questions – in which the answer is expected or 'understood'
   ● anecdote – short personal stories, memories or accounts, related to the issue
   ● humour and/or irony (where relevant).

8. Use a formal or impersonal style, although you can be emotive.

9. Either confront and provoke or soothe and reassure your audience.

10. Conclude with a repetition (reiteration) of the main point of your argument and tie up any loose ends.

Writing to Argue

Generating Ideas

Name: _____ Date: _____

Practise your skills on the following title.

Write a letter to your Headteacher, in which you argue that Year 11 students should be given more study-leave, so that they can revise more fully for their GCSE examinations and use the IT suite in school.

BRAINSTORM   Complete the lists below.

FOR:

1. Better use of IT suite.
2. Better GCSE results for the school.
3. Teachers could concentrate on those who need help most.

AGAINST:

1. Other years could not use the IT suite.
2. Less teaching time before exams.
3. Some Year 11 students would not take it seriously.

Writing to Argue

Ideas and Markers

Name: _____ Date: _____

Here is a palette of phrases and ideas you could use instead of, or as well as, any in the frame on page 7.

Phrases/sentences

I am sure that you would be only too pleased to improve the school's position in the league tables and to impress the Inspectors ...

Such a move could only have a positive effect upon the school ...

Nevertheless, the evidence would support ...

After having consulted both parents and students ...

Discourse Markers

Some of the following might also be particularly useful when you write to argue:

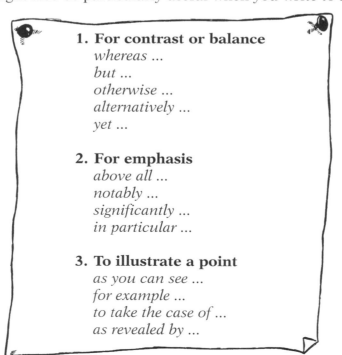

1. **For contrast or balance**
   whereas ...
   but ...
   otherwise ...
   alternatively ...
   yet ...

2. **For emphasis**
   above all ...
   notably ...
   significantly ...
   in particular ...

3. **To illustrate a point**
   as you can see ...
   for example ...
   to take the case of ...
   as revealed by ...

GCSE English Frames: Style and Purpose

 *Writing to Argue*

A Writing Frame

Name: _____ Date: _____

Use this sheet as a frame for your writing. Note the discourse markers that are being used.

In the following letter, I am going to argue the case for Year 11 students at

The first point I would like to make

On the other hand,

Can such a move be wholly positive?

An additional point

We discussed such a move and

However,

It could be argued that

Finally, I would argue that

Further Practice

Name: _____ Date: _____

Fill in the following boxes and gaps with your own school's details and your own arguments.

Dear

In the following letter, I am going to argue that Year 11 students

I am sure that you would be only too pleased to improve the school's position in the league tables and to impress the Inspectors, so here are a few of the ideas I would put forward in favour of our Year 11 students being given early study leave and enhanced use of the IT suite.

The first point I would like to make

On the other hand, it could be argued that our present Year 11 would not make use of this offer because

Nevertheless, the evidence would support the view that the school's GCSE results would improve as a result of this move and that the school would benefit in several ways. The main benefit would be

Notwithstanding this point of view, some doubters believe that

Moreover, they would argue that there would undoubtedly be
but any right-minded person would clearly see that

Is it not obvious that such a move could only have a positive effect upon the school, since

Therefore, after having consulted both parents and students, it is my opinion that only one conclusion can be reached: namely, that the students of this school

Yours

GCSE English Frames: Style and Purpose

Writing to Persuade

Key Points and Advice

Writing to persuade means that you must:

◆ try to make someone do something that they do not really want to do
◆ be aware of their reasons for not wanting to do this
◆ use lots of different ways in order to persuade them.

Writing to persuade is far more subtle than writing to argue, because you have to make someone change their mind to get your way!

Read the following points carefully before you apply them to the given title or exam question. Then work through them methodically, one by one; remember, they will form part of the Mark Scheme for your exams.

1. Writing to persuade is more one-sided than writing to argue, but it is useful to appreciate the 'other side', in order to persuade successfully.

2. To this end, you should be able to anticipate any opposition/objections.

3. You should aim to achieve varying emphasis in your answer, so brainstorming, planning and prioritising are really important.

4. The best persuasion comes via a variety of arguments.

5. Writing to persuade often uses an 'if – then' formula.

6. Use discourse markers (see the frames for possible markers).

7. Use rhetorical questions, anecdote, humour, satire and irony within context.

8. Use a more emotive style than in general: you are trying to persuade someone, after all.

9. Use an appropriate tone for your audience.

10. Conclude by repeating your most persuasive argument or arguments in a different form from the one you used earlier.

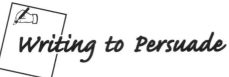

Writing to Persuade

Generating Ideas

Name: _____ Date: _____

Practise your skills on the following title.

Write a speech to be given at your next local council meeting, in which you aim to persuade the council to improve leisure facilities for young people in your area.

BRAINSTORM   Complete the lists below.

FOR:

1. Better leisure facilities would lead to fewer crimes being committed.
2. Everyone in the community would benefit.

AGAINST: (remember that it is useful to be able to counter any opposition by anticipating their possible arguments)

1. Why reward local vandals for breaking the law?
2. The money could be better spent on schools and hospitals.
3. Where would the facilities be built?

Task: Underline or number in order your most important points, so that you can prioritise them and vary your emphasis.

GCSE English Frames: Style and Purpose   © Folens (copiable page)

Writing to Persuade

Ideas and Markers

Name: _____ Date: _____

Here is a palette of further useful phrases and other useful advice for writing this persuasive speech.

Persuasive techniques

1. Try to get your audience on your side, by sharing anecdotes and by using the first person (I, me, my, we, us, etc.).

2. Repeat your really important points for maximum effect, but use this device very sparingly.

3. Attract maximum attention to your argument by varying sentence length, using a wide vocabulary and drawing on vivid images – e.g. 'a shining new sports centre'.

4. If necessary, define your terms so that your audience can understand them.

5. Make personal appeals. (In this example, you could refer to relatives of councillors; any shared knowledge; or an example of local car crime that took place recently and might have been avoided had there been such a facility.)

6. Make use of any facts and figures that could support your argument. (You can make some up in this case: most people use figures creatively!)

Here are a few more **discourse markers** to help you:

- *Whether you support this case or not ...*
- *In trying to persuade you, I would not like you to think that ...*
- *Central to this argument ...*
- *I could find many more arguments in favour, but suffice it to say that ...*
- *We all know ...*

Writing to Persuade

A Writing Frame

Name: _____ Date: _____

Use this sheet as a frame for your writing.

Good evening Lady Mayoress, councillors, ladies and gentlemen. I have come here this evening to

The main reason in favour of improving leisure facilities is that

I know that some of you would argue that

However, it would obviously be short-sighted to make this point, because

An equally compelling argument for improved facilities would be that if

then

Surely nobody could argue that

There are several further arguments that I would like to put: first,

Second,

Finally, most local residents would be greatly in favour of any such development and it would be a clear vote-winner for any councillor. Who could argue

In conclusion, I would like to summarise the main points of my argument by stating

and leaving you with the thought that

 GCSE English Frames: Style and Purpose © Folens (copiable page)

Writing to Persuade

Further Practice

Name: _____ Date: _____

One of the easiest – and most successful techniques to master in order to make your point persuasive, is to use 'The Rule of Three'. This means that you simply write an introduction; make three points; then write a conclusion.

Use this question for practice.

Write a memo to your work-experience boss, in which you try to persuade her/him that you should be given a Saturday job following your excellent work-experience report.

MEMO

I am writing this memo to ask if you would consider offering me permanent employment on Saturdays. I gained an excellent report from you; I was always punctual and I would be cheaper than more experienced staff.

First, your report stated that

Second, as you know, I was always punctual which meant that

Third, I would not want to take anybody else's job, but as most staff want a free Saturday more often; my comparative 'cheapness' might be helpful.

To sum up

and

Key Points and Advice

Writing to instruct is a very different form of writing, so you must:

◆ use a very strict frame
◆ be aware that it isn't a style designed to let you show your full range of writing skills
◆ be aware that it does not really give you as many opportunities to show off!

You will probably be given some sort of framework in the exam question, but you should also take the following points into consideration. Read them carefully, before applying them to any question. These points will form the basis of the exam Mark Scheme.

1. Planning is vitally important, so that your instructions are coherent.

2. Begin with a general statement which refers directly to the question.

3. Proceed with your instructions in a clear sequence of logical steps. Use the imperative form, where appropriate (e.g. 'Fill ...', 'Place ...').

4. Try to use discourse markers, but be aware that this is not always possible.

5. You may have the opportunity to use rhetorical questions, anecdotes, humour, satire or irony within the context of the whole, but never force them. Remember, as with discourse markers, these techniques are not always appropriate.

6. Use other organisational devices, like:

   ● number lists (1, 2, 3, etc.)
   ● bullet points.

7. Never assume any prior knowledge from your audience: lead them by the hand!

8. Use a personal style, because a confident, friendly tone will make the instructions accessible and user-friendly: instructions are meant to be understood by the reader.

9. Conclude with some sort of general point which re-states the most important aspect of the instructions.

10. The key words to remember are:

    ● clarity
    ● sequence
    ● logical steps.

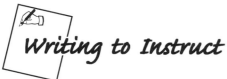

Writing to Instruct

Generating Ideas

Name: _____   Date: _____

Practise your skills on the following title.

Give instructions to a young, new car owner on how to wash a car properly. You should include the following stages:
- **equipment needed**
- **the stages to go through**
- **do's and don'ts.**

What you need when washing a car:

1. Bucket.

2. Access to plenty of hot and cold water.

The stages to go through:

1. Get rid of the worst of the dirt with a hose-pipe, or

2. Wash the car thoroughly with

Do's

1. Always use plenty of clean water.

2. Wash your car regularly.

Don'ts

1. Never rub dirt on paint-work: it is equivalent to using sand-paper.

2. Try not to use wax on glass.

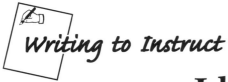

Writing to Instruct

Ideas and Markers

Name: _____   Date: _____

Here is a palette of ideas and phrases, to help you to write instructions. Discourse markers are not as important in this frame: it is the frame itself.

1. Do not waste time on drawing pictures or diagrams, but you can draw a box and label it with a description of what you would have drawn had it been an Art exam!

2. Consider the use of organisers (e.g. bullets) other than simple paragraphs when writing instructions – because examiners are asked to reward 'organisers', and not just paragraphs.

3. Make your instructions sequential and logical, without appearing to be 'mechanical'. ('Mechanical' is one of the descriptors for performance at grade 'D' in writing.) Therefore, you really must try to avoid your instructions becoming a series of plodding steps.

4. Make sure that you can write in enough detail before you start, because instructions can be mistaken for 'notes'. Plan to go into detail, and to include anecdotes, etc., if they fit in.

5. Take special note of the audience, so that you can try some humour, anecdotes, satire, etc., where relevant.

6. Use discourse markers to improve the flow and coherence of your writing.

7. Use number lists and bullet points advisedly. They can appear to be rather mechanical in the wrong situation – for example, instructions for dealing with an emotional crisis might look cold if put in bullets.

8. Use the introduction and conclusion as an opportunity to write more fluently – perhaps in longer sentences, while the logical steps between can be written in shorter, more sequential chunks.

9. If in doubt about whether the 'Writing to Instruct' choice on the exam paper will give you enough scope to hit the higher grade descriptors, then choose another option. In other words, if you think that you should be achieving a 'B' grade or above, then consider the other options before choosing 'Writing to Instruct'.

   GCSE English Frames: Style and Purpose   © Folens (copiable page)

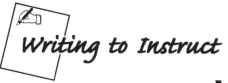

Writing to Instruct

A Writing Frame

Name: _____ Date: _____

Use this sheet as a frame for your writing. This title should allow you to use rhetorical questions, anecdotes, humour, irony or satire.

You are probably really proud of your Flash Wagon at the front of your house and you probably want to wash it to impress your friends even more. Forget the car wash and head for the bucket and water!

Here's what you will need before you start washing:
- a serviceable bucket or two
-
-

The first stage of the great car washing process is to get rid of the worst of the dirt. To do this, you can either   , or

This is the best part of the whole process as you can

On the other hand,

Second, fill your bucket with hot, soapy water and

Rinsing and drying form the final stages of the process; tasks which you can trust to a younger brother or sister whom you may wish to bring in at this point

As a conclusion, here are some do's and don'ts about washing a car.

Do

Don't

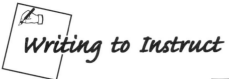

Writing to Instruct

Further Practice

Name: _____ Date: _____

In these instructions, you should fill in the gaps with your own examples of:

- discourse markers
- anecdotes
- humour
- irony
- rhetorical questions.

How to make that perfect cup of tea!

                               a tea-pot, cups, kettle, some tea and freshly drawn water. If the water is not freshly drawn from the tap, it will taste as flat as

                          boil the water in the kettle, but make sure that that you have almost twice as much as you think you'll need, because you are going to pre-heat the tea-pot. I remember when

Having preheated the tea-pot, you should now boil the kettle again. You must

                            ; if you do not, then the full flavour will not be released from the tea.

                            , the old rule of one teaspoon full per person and one for the pot, is still the best, but it does depend on taste and the type of tea in question. If you think that tea drinking is only for old people, then

Next
because if you don't, the water loses some heat and the tea leaves will not yield their full flavour.

Choice of cup is personal, but it does affect the taste of the tea. China cups

and pot mugs can

Finally,   , and enjoy your cup of tea!

Writing to Describe

Key Points and Advice

Writing to describe is the most enjoyable of all the writing tasks under examination conditions, but you must:

◆ plan to use as many descriptive techniques as possible
◆ bring your description to life and impress the examiner
◆ use the planning process like an artist with a palette.

Descriptive writing only succeeds if you are able to conjure up a picture in your reader's mind.

1. Answer the question that has been set, but be prepared to impose your own frame on the piece of writing.

2. Jot down ideas on the following things in your planning palette. Later, you can contrast aspects of them, although you don't need to use them all.

    'Colour' and atmosphere:

    ● use of senses: sight, touch, taste, hearing or smell; use of colours
    ● simile and/or metaphor.

    Choice of words and style:

    ● variety of vocabulary
    ● where you could use conversation.

    The narrative voice and setting:

    ● choose either the first person (I, me), or the third person (he, they, etc.)
    ● the time of day, year and the weather.

3. Then, when you write the 'real' thing:

    ● Make sure that you have a strong beginning and ending.
    ● *Show* rather than *tell* the reader what happens. This is descriptive writing, so plan to use a lot of images, descriptive words, or adjectives.

       E.g. Don't say *'She is lonely'* (telling).
       Say *'She sits quietly in her old chair all day staring out of the window'* (showing).

    ● Try to describe somewhere or someone that you know well, or use this as a basis for original writing.
    ● Avoid cliché ('a shiver ran down my spine').

Writing to Describe

Generating Ideas

Name: _____ Date: _____

Practise your skills on the following question.

Write a contrasting description of your school's 'play area':
- **early in the morning, before school starts**
- **at lunch-time when there are crowds of students around.**

BRAINSTORM   (Or, in this case, 'Prepare your palette')

Answer these questions: **1.** What time of year is it?   **2.** What is the weather like?
3. What can I see, hear, smell, feel, or taste?

Now prepare your palette:

	Before school	**At lunch-time**
Colours		
A simile		
A metaphor		
An effective opening sentence		
Some examples of speech		
Use of senses		

 *Writing to Describe*

Ideas and Markers

Name: _____ Date: _____

Here is a palette of phrases and ideas that you might find useful in this piece of work.

Phrases/sentences

The playground was as clean as polished steel ...

After a while, some bright yellow coats appeared ...

The bell rang at last. I could finally go inside ...

Discourse Markers

Some of the following might be useful for linking this piece of work together

1. To show where things are (prepositional devices, etc.)

next to ...
further along the yard ...
in front of the ...
coming from behind the ...
after having skirted the ...

2. Narrative Markers

now...
later on in the morning ...
after a while ...
at the end of what seemed like an ice-age ...
having waited for ...

3. Descriptive Devices

the air shone like ... (simile)
the colour of the bricks was ... (use of colour)
*the dinner hall rang, steamed, reeked, enveloped and filled me
...* (the senses)
vermilion blazers bobbed up the grey pavement (colour)

A Writing Frame

Name: _____ Date: _____

Before school:

> The playground was as clean as polished steel when I arrived: not a soul in sight and only the sound of Year 7s spoiling the peace. I could smell
>
> After a while some bright yellow coats appeared around the corner and

> I was becoming increasingly numb as the cold began to eat through my sweatshirt
>
> The bell rang at last and

At lunch-time:

> Brightly coloured wrappers blew everywhere in the swirling wind, as the
>
> Now it was hunger that threatened my very existence, as

> The warmth of the dining room hit me like a damp dish-cloth, as all of my senses were overwhelmed by the sights, sounds, smells, feelings and tastes. I saw
>
> The contrast with the fresh air was greater

> This was the memory that I would take away with me from school: the din, clash, sharpness and warmth of friendship when
>
> 'Oi! Are you coming with us, or are you going to stand there all day gawping at that wall!' Friends

Further Practice

Name: _____ Date: _____

Here is a frame for a description of a grotesquely mean character. Fill in the gaps with your own choice of descriptive words or ideas.

Arnold Swelter moved with the grace of a badly constructed
You knew which way he had come, because

Most sickeningly, he left a   of   behind him as he moved from
shop to shop. He even looked   in the way he dealt with shop assistants. Like
a blob of   , he   with everyone.

Starting at his summit, his hair was   ,   and   .
One storey lower, his face was the shape of   . Spots and pimples covered
his   and erupted   . His shirt would have made a good
                  and it had not been washed nor ironed for

Girls and young people in general tended to   because there were
many bad points about Arnold and these included   ,
but he thought he was   and that was all that mattered to him.
Swelter was so mean that

Next on the route down south of Arnold's torso came his trousers. They were held up by
          and   . Valiantly, they tried to do their job, but
          . The crotch sagged down to his   and the colour was
          . His trousers had a life of their own as they   .
It looked as if Arnold kept a   down there, and they were not happy!

The part of Arnold that touched the ground was his most   feature.
His   actually over-flowed his   trainers, giving
him the appearance of a   . Few people allowed their eyes to
flow over the full length of the Swelter frame, but   .
Arnold Swelter was a   of a man and

In the next shop was his opposite. Penny Pirrip moved with the grace of a
and was generous to a fault , especially to

Writing to Explain

Key Points and Advice

Writing to explain helps the reader to:

◆ understand processes
◆ or understand how something works.

A lot of the features are similar to other forms of writing, but there are some very important differences and structures.

Read the following points carefully and try to decide which ones are specific to this type of writing and how many are general.

1. Pay special attention to the purpose of the piece of writing.

2. Pay equal attention to your audience; unless otherwise stated, this will probably be the examiner, so take particular care.

3. Write a full and proper plan, so that your explanation has direction and shape.

4. Begin with a general statement to introduce the topic.

5. Do not simply write a sequence of events: explain *why* or *how* something happens or occurs.

6. Use the same basic structure as 'Writing to Instruct': a series of logical steps, which help to explain how or why something happens.

7. Continue these steps until the explanation is complete.

8. Use the present tense on most occasions ('it is found', 'you can see …').

9. Discourse markers showing sequence (*next, then,* etc.) and cause and effect (*As a result of,* etc.) are very useful.

10. Make your conclusion more obvious than in other pieces of writing: clearly show that this is the end of your explanation and the process itself.

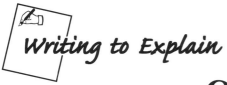

Writing to Explain

Generating Ideas

Name: _____   Date: _____

Prepare your answer to the following exam question.

You have been asked to write an entry for a new venture in your school: a Year 11 'Year Book'. In it you must explain why you have chosen your particular career path next year, and what the result might be.

BRAINSTORM   First, jot down your chosen career, or next step. Now complete the lists below:

Reasons for career choice	Results of choice
1. Parental pressure	1. This might result in resentment on your behalf later.
2. Peer group pressure	2. Not a very sensible reason for making an important career choice.

Remember to place your reasons and results in a sensible and logical order before you start:

1.

2.

3.

4.

5.

Writing to Explain

Ideas and Markers

Name: _____ Date: _____

Here is a palette of phrases, sentences and ideas for improving your grade.

Phrases/sentences

'How have I come to my decision?'

'The main reason I chose this route, was to get away from ...!'

'I remember in Year 9 when we visited ...: I decided then that I wanted to ...'

'It was hard deciding what to do, but in the end, it was as natural as summer following spring: it felt right.'

Discourse Markers

The following words and phrases occur frequently in explanations:

Sequence:

then

next

in the beginning,

after that

later

Cause and effect:

because

therefore

as a result of

an explanation could be that

the final result is that

an alternative explanation could be that

GCSE English Frames: Style and Purpose © Folens (copiable page)

 *Writing to Explain*

A Writing Frame

Name: _____ Date: _____

Use this frame for your writing.

I have been asked to explain why I chose to

To begin with, my choice of destination next year was influenced by

As a result of this, I decided that

Then I decided to discuss the matter with   , who

This resulted in

After several long discussions with a variety of other people, I felt that

In the end, I had to come to a decision, so

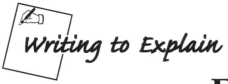

Writing to Explain

Further Practice

Name: _____ Date: _____

Practise the skill of explanatory writing, by writing about some simple processes. This is different from explaining your actions, or feelings.

1. Explain how to obtain permission to leave your school for a doctor's appointment:

Everyone has to arrange a doctor's appointment in school hours at one time or another. I will now explain how to go about it at

First of all, you must

Next you should

Finally, it is important that you

2. Give a clear explanation of why a Year 6 pupil should not fear being bullied at your school.

One of the most common fictions about starting secondary school, is that everybody is bullied. That is just not true: especially at   where we have a very clear anti-bullying policy, which I will explain to you now.

To begin with, the policy is placed in every classroom, so that

Next, in the very unlikely event that someone does bully you, you should

As a result of you telling the Year Head,

If any action is taken, then

However, very few incidents occur in a year. The evidence for this is

The final reason why you should feel safe at   , is that

GCSE English Frames: Style and Purpose © Folens (copiable page)

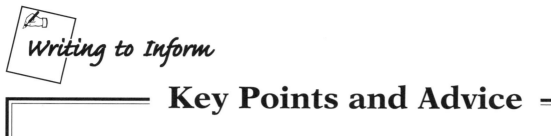

Writing to Inform

Key Points and Advice

What makes 'Writing to Inform' different from the other five forms – argue, persuade, describe, explain and instruct? Here is a list of words from a thesaurus, with similar meanings to 'inform':

◆ communicate
◆ tell
◆ to let know
◆ send word to.

These words tell us more about what this type of writing really demands: it means to *pass on some information*, which will make someone the wiser after having read it.

Read the following points, which should aid your writing of this form.

1. Use a clear introduction, or scene setting, which puts your piece of writing into context.
   E.g. *The following details set out how I came to be involved with the charity ...*

2. Give your information in a logical order, or inform somebody about events which have occurred, in the order that they occurred.

3. Finish with some form of conclusion, or closing statement, in which you refer back to the opening and make sure that you refer directly to your audience.
   E.g. *As I have indicated, this information will help you decide whether I can be of help to your company ...*

4. In most cases, use the past tense. However, do check the type of information required, as the present tense might be more appropriate.

5. Informing is an active type of writing, so you will need to include a lot of action/doing words, phrases and clauses. These verbs, and verb units of meaning, will help to drive your sentences along.

6. You should know now that discourse markers, rhetorical questions, anecdote, humour, satire and irony are all useful in context.

7. Ensure you do not slip into narrative/imaginative story-telling – there is a clear difference between informing someone about a significant event in your life and story-writing.

NOT
When we left the squalid, dirty refugee camp I felt relieved that we were free at last, and as the night stars appeared, hope sprang in my heart for our future.

BUT
We left the camp at midnight. It was a clear night, and visibility was good, which provided hope for a successful journey.

Writing to Inform

Generating Ideas (1)

Name: _____ Date: _____

There are clearly many different types of writing to inform: look up 'inform' in a thesaurus and see how many synonyms there are for this one word. We are going to concentrate on the main two types, and so include two frames:

1. Writing to inform someone else about information and detail that relates directly to you.
2. Writing to inform or tell someone about experiences or events which have a wider audience.

Let's deal with the first type of question:

BRAINSTORM

Write a letter to a possible employer, informing him/her why you think that you are the right person for the important job that you are applying for.

Write a list of reasons why you think your character makes you right for the job:

Now write a list of reasons why you think your qualifications make you right for the job:

Finally, write about the experiences which make you the best person for this job:

Task: Now, go through your lists and put your ideas in some sort of sequence or order of importance.

GCSE English Frames: Style and Purpose © Folens (copiable page)

Writing to Inform

Writing Frame (1)

I am writing to you in response to the advertisement in
on the   . I hope to give you some additional information in this letter
which will support and add to the information in my application form.

First, I feel that I am right for this job, because

Having such a character makes this the sort of job that would be particularly suitable for me
because

I also believe that my qualifications

I may not have the best grades, but the subjects that I have studied

I feel that the strongest reasons why I should be offered this job are the experiences which
I could bring to bear, if I was successful in my application.

A further piece of information I would add is that during my time as a prefect,

I hope that the additional information I have provided

 **Writing to Inform**

Generating Ideas (2)

Name: _____ Date: _____

Now we will try one of the other types of writing to inform and we will concentrate on using layout and using doing/action clauses.

Two equally important strands used in the marking of your writing are 'using structural devices/ paragraphs' and 'spelling and punctuation accuracy'. Pay special attention to these two aspects in this piece of work.

Write an article for your school newspaper in which you inform the readers about a recent educational visit, or holiday that you went on.

1. You should set out your article like a newspaper. To help you do so, write down what you will include as examples of the following presentational devices:

A headline	
A sub-heading	
'Pull-down headings'	
The first paragraph written in bold	
An interview with someone else who went on the trip	

2. Plan to use the following, if you are using a computer:

- columns
- italics or bold for emphasis
- experiment with the use of colour
- spelling and grammar checkers.

GCSE English Frames: Style and Purpose   © Folens (copiable page)

Writing Frame (2)

Name: _____   Date: _____

Inform a friend about a trip that you recently went on with school. Complete these sentences with clauses and ideas of your own.

Although I had visited   before, I

While I was in   , I learnt lots of new facts. I learnt that

I also learnt that

Furthermore, it came as something of a surprise that

What was so good about this place? I thought that

As you can see from this report, I interviewed Mr   who said, "

                                                                    ."

                            is so popular with tourists, because

If you were to visit   , you should ensure that

In addition to the aforementioned facts, I also learnt that

However, the most interesting thing which I want to inform you about is

At the end of a visit, which was in many ways very   , I should warn you that

 *Reading Non-Literary Texts*

Key Points and Advice

Frames are normally only applied to writing, but your skills as a reader will be assessed through your skills as a writer, so you have to know how to write your reading answers!

When you are looking at one text it is important you know how to:

◆ distinguish between fact and opinion
◆ follow an argument
◆ select material appropriate to purpose.

Here are some key pointers:

1. *Your reading* is being assessed, but show your awareness of the *writing skills of other writers*: the two skills of reading and writing are closely linked.

2. Remember – the criteria for your own writing and someone else's are the same:

   ● appreciation of purpose and audience
   ● structure
   ● stylistic qualities
   ● accuracy and presentation.

3. You can use bullet and number points to make your answers clearer as it is your **reading** that is being assessed, and *not* your **writing**.

4. Distinguish between the ways writers actually use facts and opinions, don't simply identify and quote them.

5. Check the 'frame' used by the writer: does he/she use rhetorical questions; anecdote; irony; structural devices; first person; humour; stylistic devices; numbers and statistics?

6. Use the same process as when you write: **read, plan/brainstorm, write and check**.

7. Finally, remember – a **fact** is something that can be proved to be true, an **opinion** is one person's viewpoint and can never be completely proven beyond all doubt.

   Example: Our latest model is the Suara 440 SLI = **Fact**
   It has a 2-litre engine, includes engine immobiliser, and air-conditioning as standard = **Facts**

   It offers a superb ride, excellent economy and style and grace to match = **Opinions**

GCSE English Frames: Style and Purpose © Folens (copiable page)

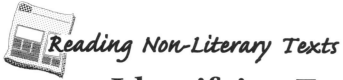

Identifying Fact and Opinion

Name: _____   Date: _____

Read the following newspaper article from *The Guardian*:

Star of Tomb Raider has weighed in to help crown a little-known London firm the planet's most successful company, reports **Chris Barrie**

Lara blasts business rivals into cyber-space

Few women in business have made an impact quite like it. But one female's outstanding talents have seen a firm little-known outside the City named the world's most successful company.

Ahead of leviathans of the business world such as Boeing, Hewlett-Packard and Merrill Lynch comes Eidos, a computer software business based in Wimbledon, south London. And the woman who made it all possible? Step forward cyber-heroine Lara Croft.

The accolade comes from an analysis of corporate growth conducted by the respected think-tank the World Economic Forum.

According to the WEF, Eidos has seen sales grow by 715 per cent to around £135 million – fuelled by the cyber-star of the electronic game, Tomb Raider.

The rating confirms Ms Croft's iconic status. Her gun-slinging antics have already been splashed across bill-boards and buses in New York. She has featured in pop videos, car advertisements in France and in such august organs as *Time* and *Newsweek* magazines.

Write your answers to the following questions by using the frame on page 36.

1. Write down one fact about the company Eidos or its products from each paragraph.   *(5 marks)*

2. Explain how you know that each one is a fact.   *(5 marks)*

3. Write down three opinions from the first two paragraphs.   *(3 marks)*

4. Explain how you know they are opinions by their use of language.   *(3 marks)*

 Reading Non-Literary Texts

A Reading Frame

Name: _____ Date: _____

---

1. The five facts that I have found out about the company, Eidos, are:

a) It has been named the world's most successful company.

b)

c)

d)

e)

---

2. The reason that I know each to be a fact is that:

a) The act of naming something can be shown to be true – the paper has named it after all!

b)

c)

d)

e)

---

3. Three opinions from the first two paragraphs are:

a) 'But one female's outstanding talents.'

b)

c)

---

4. The reason I know each to be an opinion is:

a) It is an opinion that Lara Croft has 'outstanding talents' – others might not like the game or her character.

b)

c)

GCSE English Frames: Style and Purpose © Folens (copiable page)

Following an Argument

Name: _____ Date: _____

Now read this article by Charlotte Raven from the same newspaper and answer the questions which follow by using the frame on page 38.

Anthem for Tombed youth

As I write, my new flatmate is sitting on his own in the other room, shouting at the television. "****," he will say. Or "For ***** sake". Or occasionally, "Get on with it, you *****". Every so often, he summons me to see how things are shaping up. "Charlotte," he calls, "Come here and look at this tiger." Then, when I get there: "You're too late, I already killed it."

Frustrated, I wish aloud that his assailants were less predictable. In the past two weeks, for example, we've been dealing with nothing but monkeys yet now I am supposed to be excited by one measly, unarmed tiger. To cheer me up he tells me that on the next level but one there's a seven-headed Shiva. "I'll be there in a couple of weeks," he says, as if it were remotely likely.

"Why is she there?" I asked my flatmate. "What is she meant to be doing?"

"You always ask stupid questions," he says. "You always look too deeply into things. She's there so we can play the game."

For the players using Tomb Raider guide books, the tasks are even easier. The solutions are provided. The fact that this does nothing to diminish that player's enjoyment shows how little is really required. He doesn't have to work out what to do – the answer is there on the page. Rather he must learn, by endlessly repeating the sequences, how to make Lara do what she is told. In Tomb Raider, rather scarily, the penalty for original thought is death. You gain control of the game by learning how to follow instructions. As long as you know where the monkeys are, your chances of survival are good. Sadly for my flatmate and his addled generation, life is rather harder to negotiate.

1. What do you think is Charlotte Raven's opinion about the game 'Tomb Raider'? Support your opinion by quoting from the text. *(6 marks)*

2. Explain her argument. *(8 marks)*

 Reading Non-Literary Texts

Further Practice

Name: _____ Date: _____

Now use the following frames to answer the questions on Text 2: 'Anthem for Tombed youth'.

---

1. Charlotte Raven's opinion is that the game *'Tomb Raider'*

I know this because of the way her flatmate reacts when in front of the television playing the game, he says: '   ' , which proves that

A further quotation which shows the writer's opinion is: 'Frustrated

                                                                                        '

In addition, she writes later in her article: 'Sadly

                                                                                        '

---

2. Her argument can be explained in the following points:

• She invents a clever situation at the beginning where

• The use of direct speech at the beginning

• The argument is organised by starting with

• She continues in the middle of the piece with some examples of

• Then she finishes with her own opinion, which is that

GCSE English Frames: Style and Purpose

 *Comparing Non-Literary Texts*

Key Points and Advice

The question on your English paper which asks you to compare non-literary texts may well be the hardest question in this examination and it will probably carry the highest tariff of marks.

You can compare the following aspects of two texts:

1. The **purpose** of the texts – **why** they were written.

2. The **audience** of the texts – **who** they were written for.

3. The **style** of the texts: or **how** they talk to the reader.

4. The **way they look** on the page, or their **presentation.** (This is the most obvious part of the question and the easiest to score heavily in.)

   Mention some or all of the following:

   - headlines
   - sub-headings
   - use of 'pull quotes' for emphasis
   - font
   - bold and underlining
   - pictures or other visuals
   - use of colour
   - lengths of paragraphs/sentences
   - any other obvious differences (very often you can gain marks in a question like this by stating the obvious)
   - style (lively, poetic, technical, serious, dramatic, narrative, personal, provocative, etc.).

5. **How successful** you think each text has been **in fulfilling its purpose.**

Remember! Read this type of question carefully and make sure that you answer each of the bullet points in equal detail: a plan is especially useful when comparing texts.

Comparing Non-Literary Texts

Generating Ideas (1)

Name: _____ Date: _____

Practise your skills on the following question, which refers to the articles on pages 35 and 37.

These two articles deal with the same subject, but they are different in many other ways. Compare the following aspects of both articles:

- ◆ their purpose   ◆ their style
- ◆ their audience   ◆ the way they are presented on the page.

BRAINSTORM

Item 1		**Item 2**
• to show how successful it is • to inform	**Purpose**	• to give the writer's opinion • to entertain
• business-people	**Audience**	• people in their twenties
• informative	**Style**	• anecdotal at the beginning
• in a standard newspaper style • there are	**Presentation**	• more like a magazine • it begins with

GCSE English Frames: Style and Purpose   © Folens (copiable page)

 *Comparing Non-Literary Texts*

A Reading Frame

Now compare the two articles on pages 35 and 37. This frame will help you to do this. If you do not go through the planning stage, it is difficult to compare.

First, I will compare the different purposes of the two articles. The first article sets out to show how successful

A further purpose of this article is to inform the reader

In addition

On the other hand, Charlotte Raven's purpose is very different. She gives
and
It is worth adding that this differs from the first article, because

The audience for the first article is

In comparison, the audience of the second article is more

The style of the first article is informative and relies mainly on

Whereas the second article's style begins

Both articles are taken from newspapers, but the first one is in a more standard style, with the following features

Although the second article employs a more magazine-like style, it shares similar features with the first, such as

In contrast, it also uses these different features

Comparing Non-Literary Texts

Generating Ideas (2)

Name: _____ Date: _____

You must become conversant with the terms of presentation in newspapers.

Use any national daily newspaper for this exercise. Find and cut out examples of the following presentational features. (Extracts from the two texts are given as examples, where they occur.)

This could form the basis of a piece of media coursework, as well as being useful practice for your English exam.

A headline	*'Anthem for Tombed youth'*
Sub-heading	*'Star of Tomb Raider has weighed in to help crown a little-known London firm the planet's most successful company'*
Pull-quote	
Bold print	*'Chris Barrie'*
Italics	
Underlining	
Short sentences and paragraphs	
Over-exaggerated language	*(From Text 1) 'Few women in business have made an impact quite like it.'*
Pictures/Illustrations	
An anecdote	*(From Text 2) 'As I write, my new flatmate is sitting on his own in the other room shouting at the television.'*

GCSE English Frames: Style and Purpose © Folens (copiable page)

Further Practice

Name: _____ Date: _____

Here is a comparison of the two texts. Fill in the gaps with your own answers:

Both articles deal with the same subject, but they are different in their purpose, audience, style and the way they are presented on the page.

The first comparison I would make is that they are written for very different purposes, or reasons. The first article, entitled '

' is written to   . Conversely, the second article is written to

A further point of comparison is the audience each is aimed at. The first passage is written for an audience of   , while the second is written for a   audience. The first passage uses a lot of figures like:
                            and   . The second one refers to a different generation, because at the beginning, the writer says that
and later in the article, she says

The style of the first passage is very   and
It relies upon   to make its point, and is, therefore, not as
                            as the second one which is more   because of the use
of   and
                            . As a result, the second text is   , but
they are both successful in fulfilling their purpose, in my opinion.

The way the two passages are presented on the page is very similar, but they are different in the following key areas. The font is different in the second one, because

It also looks more like a magazine article in the following ways: first,

Moreover,

Identifying What Is Being Read

═══ **Key Points and Advice** ═══

In order to gain a 'C' grade or above, you must be able to identify the following:

◆ what kind of writing it is that you are being asked to read
◆ its purpose
◆ its audience
◆ its style.

Read the following points which will help you to appreciate the different genres, purposes and styles. However, only by reading and writing widely will you fully appreciate the whole range.

1. **Look for the obvious** when reading a text: is it from a newspaper, magazine, leaflet, brochure, letter, (auto-)biography, diary, e-mail, speech, etc?

2. What **age group/audience** is the text written for?

3. What is the **purpose**, or why was it written?

4. What **features of layout** help you in this decision?

5. Are there any **stylistic devices** which help you?

6. Just like in poetry, the **style and layout should help the meaning**.

7. If it is a newspaper, is it from a **tabloid** (e.g. *The Sun, The Daily Express*, etc.) or a **broadsheet** (e.g. *The Times, The Guardian*, etc.)?

8. **How does the writer address the audience?** Does he/she use the first person (I, me, we, etc.), or the third person (he, she, they, etc.)?

9. **Does the piece of writing fit any of the frames** you have learned about? Does it write to argue, persuade, instruct, inform, explain, or describe? How can you tell?

10. When you read other texts, what **sorts of phrases give clues** to the genre? For example:

   ● 'A man is *being sought* by police'. (News report)
   ● '*Please* give *generously*.' (Charity leaflet or letter)

Identifying What Is Being Read

A Reading Frame

Name: _____   Date: _____

Look at the text, the Shelter leaflet on page 46 and answer the following questions.

1. What type of writing is this and how do you know?
2. What is its purpose?
3. Is it successful and why?

Use the frame below to help you to structure your answer.

This is a   because

and because

•

•

•

There are two reasons why it was written. The first reason is

The second reason is

The   is successful because:

•

•

•

However, it is less successful because:

•

•

•

Shelter leaflet.

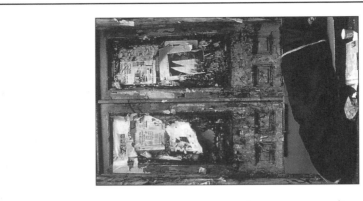

SHELTER: Practical help for homeless people

Repossession

Latest figures show that there are around 130 repossessions each working day*. Shelter Housing Aid Centres help people in this situation fight against repossession.

On the streets

The average life expectancy of somebody sleeping rough is only 42 years**. Our emergency helpline – LondonLine, soon to be extended nationwide – is open 24 hours a day giving help to people in urgent need of somewhere safe and warm to sleep.

Temporary accommodation

At the end of March 1998 there were 47,080 households living in temporary accommodation in England. Shelter is campaigning to change housing policies – to make more decent, permanent homes available to homeless people.

*Council of mortgage lenders – first half of 1998
** Source: Crisis – Still dying for a home, 1996

"I don't blame

people for walking past. Maybe they think I'm already dead ... "

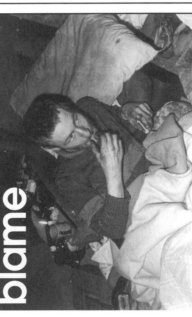

Homelessness can kill. People sleeping rough are two to three times more likely to suffer from physical health problems. Death by unnatural causes for people who sleep out can be four times more common than average, and suicide thirty-five times more likely. And did you know that around a quarter of those living rough are between 18 and 25 years old*.

But street homelessness is just the tip of the iceberg. The number of people accepted as homeless in England has increased by more than a half in the last fifteen years. And a report estimates that more than 1.5 million homes in England are unfit for human habitation.

Homelessness costs. In 1996/97 over £185 million went towards providing temporary accommodation for homeless households. And the health problems suffered by people living on the street and in poor housing puts extra pressure on the health service. Shelter believes that it makes economic sense in the long term to provide decent housing for homeless people.

It's not about politics, it's about getting homeless people decent homes, and off the streets. But to tackle Britain's housing crisis effectively we have to keep in touch with public opinion.

Please spend just two minutes of your time completing this survey. We would also be very grateful if you could consider making a donation of £15 – or whatever you can afford – to support Shelter's work with homeless people. Please let us have your answers within 14 days.

Thank you.

*Source: The Rough Sleeping Report. The Social Exclusions Unit – July 1998

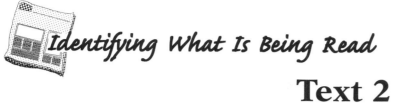

Identifying What Is Being Read

Text 2

Name: _____ Date: _____

Here is a very different type of text. It is part of Martin Luther King's 1963 speech given at the Washington rally for equal rights.

"I say to you today, my friends, that in spite of the difficulties and frustrations of the moment I still have a dream. I have a dream that one day this nation will rise up and live out the true meaning of its creed: 'We hold these truths to be self-evident: that all men are created equal.' 5

"I have a dream that one day on the red hills of Georgia the sons of former slaves and the sons of former slave-owners will be able to sit down together at the table of brotherhood.

"I have a dream that one day even the state of Mississippi, a state sweltering with the heat of injustice, sweltering with the heat of 10 oppression will be transformed into an oasis of freedom and justice.

"I have a dream that my four little children will one day live in a nation where they will not be judged by the color of their skin, but by the content of their character.

• • •

"And if America is to be a great nation, this must become true. So let freedom ring from the 15 prodigious hilltops of New Hampshire. Let freedom ring from the mighty mountains of New York. Let freedom ring from the heightening Alleghenies of Pennsylvania!

• • •

"When we let freedom ring from every village and every hamlet, from every state and every city, we will be able to speed up that day when all God's children, black men and white men, Jews and Gentiles, Protestants and Catholics, will be able to join hands and sing in the words of that old 20 Negro spiritual, 'Free at last! Thank God almighty, we are free at last.'"

1. What was the purpose of this speech?

2. What was the audience of this speech?

3. What rhetorical devices were used in this speech?
(Or, in other words, how do you know that this is a speech?)

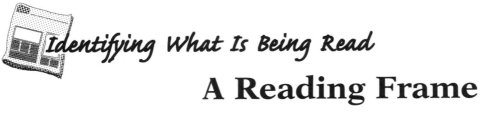

Identifying What Is Being Read

A Reading Frame

Name: _____   Date: _____

Look at Martin Luther King's speech on page 47.

1. The purpose of this speech was to

2. There were several audiences for this speech. The primary audience was

There was also a wider audience which Martin Luther King could reach

In addition, the manner of the speech and its content meant it was also important because

3. The rhetorical devices that the speaker used were repetition (an example of which is
), in order to

He also addresses his audience directly in line   , with the result that

He uses heightened or symbolic language when he says

He does this because

He refers to his own personal situation in order to gain the audience's sympathy, when he

In addition, he uses contrast when he

This shows that

A final device was to pair examples, like   , in order to

GCSE English Frames: Style and Purpose   © Folens (copiable page)